Know Yourself &
Take Flight

31 Days to Becoming
Out of Reach

Yvette Malveaux

Book Completion Services Provided by:
TRU Statement Publications www.trustatementpublications.com

www.trustatementpublications.com

Contents

INTRODUCTION 1

SENSE OF PURPOSE..1

DO YOU KNOW HOW ABSOLUTELY AMAZING YOU ARE? 2

KEEPING THE MAIN THING, ...3

THE MAIN THING 3

LISTEN TO YOURSELF 4

INSTRUCTIONS.. 5

COMPLETE DAILY SELF-CHECKS...5

MAKE DECISIONS 7

LEARN SELF-LOVE, AWARENESS, AND ACCEPTANCE 9

ENCOURAGE, MOTIVATE, AND INSPIRE YOURSELF 12

SEIZE THE MOMENT 13

TRUST YOURSELF 14

GET STARTED 16

DAY ONE 19

THE SCARY UNCOMFORTABLE THINGS....................................19

Self-Check..24

DAY TWO 27

MAKING DECISIONS..27

Self-Check..33

DAY THREE 37

I AM 100% AMAZING 37

Self-Check..39

DAY FOUR 43

I BELIEVE IN MYSELF 43

Self-Check..48

DAY FIVE 51

I WILL SEIZE THE MOMENT 51

Self-Check..56

DAY SIX **59**

    TRUSTING MYSELF 59

        Self-Check 64

DAY SEVEN **67**

    I ACCEPT MYSELF 67

        Self-Check 72

DAY EIGHT **75**

    I INSPIRE MYSELF 75

        Self-Check 80

DAY NINE **83**

    LEARNING THE TRUTH ABOUT MYSELF 83

        Self-Check 88

DAY TEN **91**

    MY GRACE AND ABILITIES 91

        Self-Check 96

DAY ELEVEN **99**

    THE SOUND OF MY VOICE 99

        Self-Check 104

DAY TWELVE **107**

    ANYTHING IS POSSIBLE 107

        Self-Check 112

DAY THIRTEEN **115**

    IN MY LIFETIME 115

        Self-Check 120

DAY FOURTEEN **123**

    EMBRACING WHAT MAKES ME HAPPY 123

        Self-Check 128

DAY FIFTEEN **131**

    EMBRACING MY UNIQUENESS 131

        Self-Check 136

DAY SIXTEEN..**139**

    I am Evolving 139

        Self-Check *144*

DAY SEVENTEEN **147**

    My Priorities 147

        Self-Check *152*

DAY EIGHTEEN **155**

    I am Heard 155

        Self-Check *160*

DAY NINETEEN **163**

    I am Fulfilled 163

        Self-Check *168*

DAY TWENTY **171**

    Being Honest with Myself 171

        Self-Check *176*

DAY TWENTY-ONE **179**

    Looking Ahead 179

        Self-Check *184*

DAY TWENTY-TWO **187**

    Identifying my Qualities 187

        Self-Check *192*

DAY TWENTY-THREE **195**

    I Won't be Held Down...195

        Self-Check *200*

DAY TWENTY-FOUR **203**

    Modifying my Future 203

        Self-Check *208*

DAY TWENTY-FIVE **211**

    How I See Myself 211

        Self-Check *216*

DAY TWENTY-SIX **219**

    MAKING A PLAN 219

        Self-Check *224*

DAY TWENTY-SEVEN **227**

    FACING MY FEARS 227

        Self-Check *232*

DAY TWENTY-EIGHT **235**

    LOVING MY YOUNGER SELF 235

        Self-Check *240*

DAY TWENTY- NINE **243**

    I ENJOY MY LIFE 243

        Self-Check *248*

DAY THIRTY **251**

    I AM LIVING IN MY NOW 251

        Self-Check *256*

DAY THIRTY-ONE **259**

    I AM SUCCESSFUL 259

        Self-Check *264*

THE UNLOAD ZONE **267**

This Journal is as much for me as it is for those who find it of use to them. It has been written with the intent to bring you to your highest awareness of self.

INTRODUCTION

Sense of Purpose

Do you know what God put you on this earth to do? For me, I love what I do, and I want to do it as much as possible. But before I got to this place in life, I studied, and studied, then studied some more about myself. I learned I wanted to always give more than I thought I could. When things didn't seem to go right, I could see them as opportunities to learn what I am made of, and questions were formed to remind myself of what I learned.

Do I stand by the principles I share with others? The things I believe as truths? And that God is in control? What was the Genesis for me? Who inspired me to this point when I face adversity? Do I look at situations as a challenge or opportunity? Where did that come from? Where did I learn that from? Who inspired me to the point of not giving up when I face adversity?

As I learned more about myself, I developed a need to inspire and show others that there are real people who believe and will make a stand for what they believe – which is what I was already doing. I had to make a decision to be great at what I was doing. That's a decision we all must make.

My goal is to equip as many people as possible by helping

them find and know their value. I am talking to those who say, "I want more. I want another level of self-awareness; not just in a church building, but as a way of life." What you are looking for is beyond a once in a while experience in church or with church people. You need to own your experience to the point that it is always with you, wherever you go. It's finding out who you are as a person and what you can do. Knowing you can go beyond your mental limitations. It doesn't matter what others are doing. You should consistently ask yourself, "What am I doing?"

Do You Know How Absolutely Amazing You Are?

I have never met anyone that wasn't interesting; however, their light may have been subdued on a low burn, but never completely out. I like to think of myself as a lighter. I either cause a low flame to burn high or a high flame to become an inferno. Either way, I want to leave people with a great experience after meeting me.

I am the author of this journal and I find that knowing yourself is a game changer that can take you on an adventure to a fulfilling life. In this journal the goal is to begin laying a road map that leads directly to you. Learning to navigate, especially through tough terrain, builds lasting character and paves the way to show it can be conquered and you can make it through.

This moment, right here and right now, is where you start

your journey. It's important to be consistent, to stay even and balanced. The best revenge is to live your own life, never imitating anyone, causing you to lose yourself or your authenticity. Be the best you, give your all. Tap into your God given abilities.

Keeping the Main Thing, the Main Thing

My philosophy is... *"Don't give up. Train and Discipline yourself to do things the right way. Personal Integrity Matters. Don't lie to yourself about where you really are and don't leave God out."*

Training tells your brain to stay prepared – Always. Real sharpness comes with effort. You must apply yourself. You must want to be great. You must push through the tough times. Always be willing to learn. It will get you where you're going. Give everything your best effort. Always strive to get better. Use yourself to display greatness and determination in an active way that leaves a trail for others to walk on. Demand respect with your actions and diligence. Know that it is your time to ELEVATE.

The word Elevate is a verb, and a verb is an action; it means to Raise, Promote, Upgrade. So, this is your time to rise to an impressive level. You can't just sit around; you've got to do the work. Take the good with the bad. You must make new life choices and know everybody is not going to stay your friend throughout your process.

Eventually, you will have your own questions and will go further than what you knew was possible. Every moment you make time to look within yourself, expect to discover that you have so much potential to soar. Enjoy your inward path to the treasure hidden in your earthen vessel.

Listen to Yourself

When you show up in your own life and are adamant about making the necessary shift into your potentiality, the doors swing open and the pages in your life turn. You begin the best days of your own life.

Enjoy your journey into the inner dimensions of yourself. There is so much you have been wanting to tell yourself about yourself. Learn the sound of your own voice and trust it to answer the difficult things you have avoided.

Yvette Malveaux

INSTRUCTIONS

Complete Daily Self-Checks

Sometimes, we forget how we feel when we're constantly focused on just getting through the day, whether it's at home, work, or elsewhere. We can lose track of ourselves and what we think and feel. We can lose track of our personal goals, as well. Completing daily self-checks will guide you towards a healthy, positive, and non-obsessive way to check in with yourself on how you think and feel. Journaling your self-discoveries allows you to bring healthy viable solutions and answers to the surface, and back into a healthy place within yourselves that will positively affect everything else around you, as well.

The self-check is a series of guided questions to keep you talking and thinking about yourself. Not blaming or passing your situations, thoughts, or feelings to anyone else; reaffirming your ability to change your course. As you journal daily, you will be asking yourself important questions that are more solution oriented than why oriented, such as, "What are you going to do about it?"

We have the ability to change our situations and circumstances. We can change our thought process and that's one of the many goals to reach in this journey of getting back to yourself.

The biggest check is to watch how you speak to yourself. Your thoughts about yourself are so important. When you find yourself spiraling down or in a negative depressed mode, find scriptures from the Bible to help you reroute your thoughts to what God has already spoken concerning you. There are many practical things that God has said. We need to stop slapping bandages on everything and heal for real. When looking in the Bible, we find the scriptures that counter what has been holding us down, and in most cases holding us back.

Your self-check focus should literally be on fixing things and moving on. Ask yourself, "What are you gonna do about it?" Solutions, Solutions, Solutions. You have the answers. You need to trust your decisions, tempered in truth. Truth, meaning you are looking at yourself too, not just blaming everyone and everything else. See how you have contributed to what has been going on in your life; then readjust and reroute the course to your purpose and passion.

Self-checks will also take the power away from your distractions and stagnation to help you refocus on where you're headed in fulfilling your individuality and passion. When what you really want to do is suppressed, it tends to bring about a form of depression and you can begin to feel boxed in. We will all experience moments of feeling unhappy when we are not doing things that bring out our highest qualities. When we're doing things that block us from expressing the best version of what we are capable of doing, or have decided to do, we feel suppressed.

One of the causes is due to not following our heart's desire. It creates the feeling that something huge is missing in our lives. When we're out of alignment and give up our dreams and passions, we get locked into things we are not passionate about and we shut down. Your daily self-checks will reconnect you with your personal passion and what you were meant to do, guiding you back to your epicenter – back to yourself.

Remember, you are born with a purpose and a plan (Jeremiah 29:11). Everyone is a letter, written directly from God. If we all could grasp that the Word of God is a *mirror* that reflects who we truly are, and it holds the realities of our potential to be magnificent, we would see we are a reflection of our creator in a tangible expression, right here and right now.

The most attractive person is a person getting closer to God in a healthy personal relationship. That person wants to shine and isn't intimidated when other's shine just as bright or brighter.

Make Decisions

Decision is the act of choosing between two or more courses of action in your process of problem solving. It includes choosing between practical solutions to resolve a problem. Sometimes, it's through reason, an intuitive process, or even a combination of the two to gather as much information as you can, both positively and negatively, about it to make an informed decision that is best for you.

When you become intentional about making daily decisions, you become proactive in your life. Remember, this journey is your personal journal to learn more about yourself, making choices on what will and won't work for you can change the trajectory of your life.

To be honest, we can never escape making choices. We make them every day and all the time. Some are good and some are bad; either way, we find that we must make decisions. It's a life skill we are taught very early on in our lives, and we soon learn that all our choices have consequences. The biggest consequence to making decisions is to be stuck in indecision. Indecision is a type of passive approach, allowing whatever that comes your way just to come, you do nothing to accept or deflect it, and you become a non-participant in your own life and outcomes.

The bible says choose wisely and to stay grounded when making decisions (Proverbs 11:2). The bible uses real life examples of choosing wisely through application of scripture. 1 Corinthians 15:33 (ESV) says, "Do not be deceived; bad company ruins good morals." Proverbs 12:26 (ESV) states, "One who is righteous is a guide to his neighbor, but the way of the wicked leads them astray." It takes an honorable man to admit a mistake, and it takes a lot of courage to reverse the course after making a poor choice.

Learn Self-Love, Awareness, and Acceptance

Self-love is a rearguard for one's own well-being and happiness. Self-love also helps you to understand yourself, accept yourself, and have a healthy self-esteem. When we are aware of ourselves, we have a better understanding of who we are, and we are able to experience our own uniqueness.

Self-love is your starting point to showing others love. It helps you to become selfless and allows you to see everyone as having the potential to be great. Self-love teaches you how to open the door for someone else so they can keep going and won't give up. Self-love is the foundation of all good relationships.

A genius minded friend of mine once told me, "You can't truly love someone unless you love yourself, and you can't give away what you don't have." These words were a big contribution to my journal writing. The goal is to love yourself so much that the love you possess overflows onto others around you.

Some of your best strengths and qualities are revealed in the little things you do. Paying attention to the details about yourself can go a long way. You have the ability to learn from your mistakes, prioritize your life, improve your communication skills, and use your time to create a better outcome for your current situations. These suggestions are minor adjustments that bring about phenomenal benefits to your life.

Self-acceptance is liberating. You become free from being overly concerned about what other people think about you and at the same time you lose that judgmental way you have thought about others. This frees you from the negative things you, at one time, believed other people thought about you. You can move on to do what you need to do to make things better in your life. On a final note it does not mean that you accept the lesser version of who you are and do nothing to change and improve. It also doesn't mean accepting your life as it is; this is about recognizing and doing what it takes to get better and do better.

Below are a few things that can help you in the area of Self-acceptance:

1. Give yourself permission to follow your heart. Give yourself a chance to lead your own life.

2. Write in your journal but focus on your story; how you feel, how you think, and your plan of action to fix things or just make things better.

3. Love and embrace yourself as you are. Don't try to be like anyone else.

Take comfort in knowing that the scriptures God gave us reminds us of His acceptance of us. Psalms 139:17-18 starts with *How precious are your thoughts about me.* Psalm 139:14-16 says we are *fearfully and wonderfully made.* Ephesians 2:10 says *we are his workmanship created in Christ Jesus for good works.* Romans 9:20 states *we don't say to the molder why have you made me like this.* There are many to be read in the bible. But one more I'd like you to know as a personal scripture is 1 Corinthians 13:4-8 (ESV),

> *Love is patient and kind; love does not envy or boast; it is not arrogant or rude. It does not insist on its own way; it is not irritable or resentful; it does not rejoice at wrongdoing but rejoices with the truth. Love bears all things, believes all things, hopes all things, endures all things. Love never ends. As for prophecies, they will pass away; as for tongues, they will cease; as for knowledge, it will pass away.*

Show yourself the love of God, not just to others, as it's laid out in this passage. This can be a guidepost for a transformation in the way you handle yourself.

Encourage, Motivate, and Inspire Yourself

Self-encouragement and self-motivation are powerful allies. They involve you creating a safe space, around yourself, with people who encourage you instead of finding fault with you; people who aren't threatened by your successes. With self-encouragement, you focus more on things you have accomplished and less on things you haven't. Being self-motivated helps you achieve your goals. Self-encouragement and self-motivation are important because you're less likely to give up on yourself.

Believing in yourself affects everything you do. It's important that you get control of your narrative. Stop putting your value in the hands of others to evaluate for you. Stop letting others write your story. Most people mean well, but make bad choices pertaining to you. They project themselves and their views onto you as though they have your best intentions in mind, without knowing who you really are and the direction your life is headed. So, you must know and believe in yourself. In other words, learn to trust your personal instincts about your own life.

By taking the initiative and power to act on your own behalf, you become your own inspiration and will inspire others in the process. When you inspire someone, you give them courage to do something they have already desired to do. Below are a few examples of how to inspire others and yourself:

1. Listen to what's being said. Your conversations go both ways.

2. Express love and appreciation openly, and nurture equality.

3. Believe in collective power. When somebody else is excelling it shouldn't intimidate you. You're genuinely celebrating their success without hesitation.

4. You set a tone to always do and be the best version of yourself.

5. Teach and share everything so people can have all the information they need to excel and succeed in what they are doing.

Seize the Moment

Seizing the moment means taking full advantage of opportunities, whenever and wherever they present themselves. It's about living life to your full potential, taking the necessary chances to see if something is for you or not, and being present in your moments and taking it all in. The best way to seize the moment is to feel what you feel without the fear you're handling yourself the wrong way.

Trust Yourself

Self-trust is so important. It means you believe in yourself to make the decisions and choices you need to make for and about you. It also means you refuse to give up on yourself. The thoughts and actions you have about yourself are encouraging and uplifting and will get you through the tough moments. Understanding those tough moments are temporary.

Trust is the foundation of all meaningful relationships. Trusting yourself is so important to your intimacy with knowing yourself better. You can't skip over this. You may have some disappointments on this journey, but it is still an opportunity to know yourself better. So, with this in mind I would say to you, "You have to make the choice to jump back in. Let your guard down and let go of fear."

There are many suggestions to point you in the direction of trusting yourself. Below are a few examples. You may add things to the list as you discover and learn more about yourself – and that's a great addition to knowing who you are.

1. Be yourself.

2. Be truthful with yourself.

3. Choose to forgive yourself for past and present mistakes.

4. Spend time with yourself.

5. Set reasonable goals that you can accomplish and be excited about their completion.

6. Embrace yourself, your strengths, and your vulnerabilities.

7. Be decisive.

Being over consumed with regretting things you have done and decisions you have made, to the point you're beating yourself up and thinking you're not doing good enough, is an example of not trusting yourself. Below are just a few signs that may indicate there are trust issues and are pointing you in the direction of finding your truth.

1. I have a hard time recognizing, understanding, or believing in my innate value and worth.

2. I avoid commitment of any kind.

3. I am very defensive all the time.

4. I do things to prove myself and value to others.

5. I minimize or deny my own needs.

6. Sometimes it's difficult to recognize the truth from a lie. Making it difficult to make decisions.

Turning these negative declarations into positive statements will give yourself permission to heal, as well as the grace to make mistakes and know they can be fixed or changed to better choices that you have discovered works for you.

Here are a few fix it tips to help you in your process. I'm sure you will discover many more on your own journey to knowing yourself.

1. Let people know what you need and be direct about it.

2. Give people a chance to show you who they are before you jump into anything that locks you in with them.

3. Learn how to have open-ended conversations that allow for disagreement.

4. Focus on your growth, even if they are baby steps, so they become strides in your personal growth.

5. Keep promises to yourself. Follow through for you.

Get Started

This journal is designed for you to complete a daily self-check, every day for the next 31 days. Even if it is just for a moment, your daily self-check is to see how you are and where you are in your self-discovery journey.

The daily sections in this journal are designed to encourage you and prompt you to think and focus on yourself. Your self-discovery is to assure you of what you already knew about yourself, and wow you about the things you have yet to learn.

For You, About You
Let the Journal Journey Begin...

Always
Leave Room for Your
Plans and Ideas
To be Dreamed, Imagined,
Executed, and Created.

~Yvette Malveaux

Day One

The Scary Uncomfortable Things

Everyone has a closet. You may say, "What closet?" The one you don't like to acknowledge that exists.

Sometimes we hide the real us in there, or we put things in there that have hurt us, so we're not identified by the incidents that took place in our lives. It's the one with the things we are ashamed of – That Closet.

Cleaning out your closet simply means acknowledging the things you have stored in there and letting it all go. Sometimes it means having a hard conversation, once and for all. Either way, get that stuff out of your way so you can move on.

No more storing the baggage. Scream! Shout! Cry! But don't you dare stay in that place. You opened the closet for one purpose, to get rid of what has been keeping you from your greatest potential and purposes. That closet has been keeping you from your freedom, which you so desperately want to experience. Say goodbye and part ways with that closet. If it's *you* that you have stuffed in that closet – Forgive yourself. Forgive others if you held onto their atrocities and were not able to discover your world without the damages they caused. I'm not saying forget, I am saying you have the power to experience what can happen with where you're headed now. If you keep those things in your closet, the memories of what you haven't let go will always pull you back to it. So, it's imperative that you deal with your stuff in that closet so you can be truly free from the dread of repeating the same cycles.

Now, let's empty that closet.

Below and on the following pages, make a list of all the items you have stored or hidden in your closet. These items can be experiences, emotions, thoughts, or ideas; but keep in mind, only you know what you are keeping in your closet, so don't be limited to this list.

_____

_____

_____

_____

_____

_____

_____

_____

_____

_____

_____

_____

_____

_____

Self-Check

*How Do You Feel Right Now?
Write About It.*

_____

_____

_____

_____

_____

_____

_____

_____

_____

_____

_____

_____

_____

_____

_____

_____

_____

My Value Has Gone Up Since Knowing You. I Figure I'm Pretty Valuable. I Never Quite Thought That About Myself Before. I Didn't Know I Was Able to Negotiate Myself as The Focal Point.

~Yvette Malveaux

Day Two

Making Decisions

What decision did I make today?

_____

_____

_____

_____

_____

_____

_____

_____

_____

_____

_____

_____

_____

_____

_____

_____

_____

_____

_____

What was I wrong about?

_____

_____

_____

_____

_____

_____

_____

_____

_____

_____

_____

_____

_____

_____

_____

_____

_____

What was I right about?

_____

_____

_____

_____

_____

_____

_____

_____

_____

_____

_____

_____

_____

_____

_____

_____

_____

_____

_____

_____

_____

What was out of my control?

_____

_____

_____

_____

_____

_____

_____

_____

_____

_____

_____

_____

_____

_____

_____

_____

_____

_____

_____

What was within my control?

_____

_____

_____

_____

_____

_____

_____

_____

_____

_____

_____

_____

_____

_____

_____

_____

_____

_____

_____

Self-Check

How Do You Feel Right Now?
Write About It.

_____

_____

_____

_____

_____

_____

_____

_____

_____

_____

_____

_____

_____

_____

_____

_____

Goodness in Action

Let People Know Each One of Them is Precious.

~Yvette Malveaux

Day Three

I am 100% Amazing

Write Down 5 Amazing Things That You Like About Yourself.

1._____

_____

_____

2._____

_____

_____

3._____

_____

_____

4._____

_____

_____

5._____

_____

_____

Self-Check

How Do You Feel Right Now?
Write About It.

_____

_____

_____

_____

_____

_____

_____

_____

_____

_____

_____

_____

_____

_____

_____

_____

_____

I Hope to Give You Tools That Assist in the Ability to Make You Think About Your Own Life.

~Yvette Malveaux

Day Four

I Believe in Myself

Write Yourself an Encouraging Letter About Believing in Yourself.

_____

_____

_____

_____

_____

_____

_____

_____

_____

_____

_____

_____

_____

_____

_____

_____

_____

_____

Self-Check

How Do You Feel Right Now?
Write About It.

_____

_____

_____

_____

_____

_____

_____

_____

_____

_____

_____

_____

_____

_____

_____

_____

Secrets... Things in the Heart That Don't Get Expressed... Maybe Because it Makes You Feel Vulnerable.

~Yvette Malveaux

Day Five

I Will Seize the Moment

Write an Encouraging Letter to Yourself About Seizing the Moment.

_____

_____

_____

_____

_____

_____

_____

_____

_____

_____

_____

_____

_____

_____

_____

_____

Self-Check

How Do You Feel Right Now?
Write About It.

_____

_____

_____

_____

_____

_____

_____

_____

_____

_____

_____

_____

_____

_____

Watch This!
Are You watching?

Great, Because Great Teachers
Were Once Great Students.

Meet You at The Top!

~Yvette Malveaux

Day Six

Trusting Myself

Write Yourself an Encouraging Letter About Trusting Yourself.

_____

_____

_____

_____

_____

_____

_____

_____

_____

_____

_____

_____

_____

_____

_____

_____

_____

_____

_____

Self-Check

How Do You Feel Right Now?
Write About It.

_____

_____

_____

_____

_____

_____

_____

_____

_____

_____

_____

_____

_____

_____

_____

_____

Who Cares What They think?

What Do YOU Think?

~Yvette Malveaux

Day Seven

I Accept Myself

Write an Encouraging Letter to Yourself About Accepting Yourself.

_____

_____

_____

_____

_____

_____

_____

_____

_____

_____

_____

_____

_____

_____

_____

_____

_____

_____

Self-Check

How Do You Feel Right Now? Write About It.

_____

_____

_____

_____

_____

_____

_____

_____

_____

_____

_____

_____

_____

_____

_____

_____

Ability is When You Have Just Decided, if I Perish, I Perish, But I'm Gonna Do Something About This Situation.

~Yvette Malveaux

Day Eight

I Inspire Myself

Write an Encouraging Letter to Yourself About Inspiring Yourself.

_____

_____

_____

_____

_____

_____

_____

_____

_____

_____

_____

_____

_____

_____

_____

_____

_____

Self-Check

How Do You Feel Right Now?
Write About It.

_____

_____

_____

_____

_____

_____

_____

_____

_____

_____

_____

_____

_____

_____

_____

_____

You Must Commit to
Doing What's Necessary
to Not Lose Your True Self
to the Abrasiveness of
This External Realm. But
Stay Grounded in God
Who is Able to Keep You
From Falling (Jude 24-25).

~Yvette Malveaux

Day Nine

Learning the Truth
about Myself

Do You Know What Lies You Have Believed About Yourself? List the lies you have discovered.

_____

_____

_____

_____

_____

_____

_____

_____

_____

_____

_____

_____

_____

_____

_____

_____

_____

_____

_____

Replace the lies with the truths you know about yourself.

_____

_____

_____

_____

_____

_____

_____

_____

_____

_____

_____

_____

_____

_____

_____

_____

_____

_____

Self-Check

How Do You Feel Right Now?
Write About It.

_____

_____

_____

_____

_____

_____

_____

_____

_____

_____

_____

_____

_____

_____

_____

_____

What Will You Do to Ensure YOU Have Space in Your Life for The Real Authentic You?

It's Going to Take Self Commitment in a World That Uses People to the MAX.

~Yvette Malveaux

Day Ten

My Grace and Abilities

What is Your God-Given Grace and Abilities?

_____

_____

_____

_____

_____

_____

_____

_____

_____

_____

_____

_____

_____

_____

_____

_____

_____

_____

What Will You Do to Display Your God-Given Grace and abilities?

_____

_____

_____

_____

_____

_____

_____

_____

_____

_____

_____

_____

_____

_____

_____

_____

_____

Self-Check

How Do You Feel Right Now?
Write About It.

_____

_____

_____

_____

_____

_____

_____

_____

_____

_____

_____

_____

_____

_____

_____

_____

_____

I Know a Person, Who Knows a Person, Who Saw Another Person Go on to Do Great Things in Their Lifetime. Did You Know You Are That Person? Yes, You The One This Is All About.

~Yvette Malveaux

Day Eleven

The Sound of My Voice

Can You Hear Your Voice?
What are you saying to yourself?

_____

_____

_____

_____

_____

_____

_____

_____

_____

_____

_____

_____

_____

_____

_____

_____

_____

Self-Check

How Do You Feel Right Now?
Write About It.

_____

_____

_____

_____

_____

_____

_____

_____

_____

_____

_____

_____

_____

_____

_____

_____

Give Away Everything You Know.
Cause People to Grow.

~Yvette Malveaux

Day Twelve

Anything is Possible

What Makes YOU feel like anything is possible?

_____

_____

_____

_____

_____

_____

_____

_____

_____

_____

_____

_____

_____

_____

_____

_____

_____

_____

Self-Check

How Do You Feel Right Now?
Write About It.

_____

_____

_____

_____

_____

_____

_____

_____

_____

_____

_____

_____

_____

_____

_____

_____

_____

Focus on Adorning the Inside of Your Soul. Dressing Up the Outside Only Avoids the Real Issues at Hand.

~Yvette Malveaux

Day Thirteen

In My Lifetime

What is Something YOU want to achieve in your lifetime.

_____

_____

_____

_____

_____

_____

_____

_____

_____

_____

_____

_____

_____

_____

_____

_____

_____

_____

Self-Check

How Do You Feel Right Now?
Write About It.

_____

_____

_____

_____

_____

_____

_____

_____

_____

_____

_____

_____

_____

_____

_____

_____

On the Right Day, You Could Have Words That Could Change Someone's Life.

~Yvette Malveaux

Day Fourteen

Embracing What Makes

Me Happy.

What is something YOU really enjoy doing and why?

Self-Check

How Do You Feel Right Now?
Write About It.

_____

_____

_____

_____

_____

_____

_____

_____

_____

_____

_____

_____

_____

_____

_____

_____

_____

_____

Give a Moment of Respect for All Those Who Loved Us in Our Beginning.

~Yvette Malveaux

Day Fifteen

Embracing my Uniqueness

What makes YOU really stand out?

_____

_____

_____

_____

_____

_____

_____

_____

_____

_____

_____

_____

_____

_____

_____

_____

_____

_____

_____

_____

_____

Self-Check

How Do You Feel Right Now? Write About It.

_____

_____

_____

_____

_____

_____

_____

_____

_____

_____

_____

_____

_____

_____

_____

_____

_____

_____

Choose How to Respond Instead of Just Responding.

~Yvette Malveaux

Day Sixteen

I am Evolving

What habit would YOU like to change?

_____

_____

_____

_____

_____

_____

_____

_____

_____

_____

_____

_____

_____

_____

_____

_____

_____

_____

_____

Self-Check

How Do You Feel Right Now?
Write About It.

_____

_____

_____

_____

_____

_____

_____

_____

_____

_____

_____

_____

_____

_____

_____

I work on it all the time. That's what makes it obtainable.

~Yvette Malveaux

Day Seventeen

My Priorities

What is priority for YOU right now?

_____

_____

_____

_____

_____

_____

_____

_____

_____

_____

_____

_____

_____

_____

_____

_____

_____

Self-Check

How Do You Feel Right Now?
Write About It.

_____

_____

_____

_____

_____

_____

_____

_____

_____

_____

_____

_____

_____

_____

_____

_____

_____

Learn How to Turn the Light on in Yourself. Then Turn on The Light in Every Human Being.

~Yvette Malveaux

Day Eighteen

I am Heard

When is the last time someone truly listened to YOU?

Self-Check

How Do You Feel Right Now?
Write About It.

_____

_____

_____

_____

_____

_____

_____

_____

_____

_____

_____

_____

_____

_____

_____

_____

Make Sure...
All Your Conversations
Have A Purpose with Content,
Intent, and With A Clear Road Map
to Elevation and Success...

(Or Just Don't Say Anything)

~Yvette Malveaux

Day Nineteen

I am Fulfilled

What is something presently in YOUR life that gives YOU a sense of Fulfillment?

_____

_____

_____

_____

_____

_____

_____

_____

_____

_____

_____

_____

_____

_____

_____

_____

_____

_____

_____

Self-Check

How Do You Feel Right Now?
Write About It.

_____

_____

_____

_____

_____

_____

_____

_____

_____

_____

_____

_____

_____

_____

_____

_____

_____

Courage is Ability

on Display

~Yvette Malveaux

Day Twenty

Being Honest with Myself

What is something YOU dumbed down or lied to yourself about and why?

_____

_____

_____

_____

_____

_____

_____

_____

_____

_____

_____

_____

_____

_____

_____

_____

_____

Self-Check

How Do You Feel Right Now?
Write About It.

_____

_____

_____

_____

_____

_____

_____

_____

_____

_____

_____

_____

_____

_____

_____

_____

Don't Talk Yourself Out of Your Personal Greatness...

(Everybody Has Their Own)

~*Yvette Malveaux*

Day Twenty-One

Looking Ahead

What do YOU look forward to every week?

_____

_____

_____

_____

_____

_____

_____

_____

_____

_____

_____

_____

_____

_____

_____

_____

_____

Self-Check

How Do You Feel Right Now?
Write About It.

_____

_____

_____

_____

_____

_____

_____

_____

_____

_____

_____

_____

_____

_____

_____

_____

DON'T EVER GIVE UP

BE CONFIDENT

BE INSPIRED

BE YOURSELF

~Yvette Malveaux

Day Twenty-Two

Identifying my Qualities

What do YOU have to offer someone else?

_____

_____

_____

_____

_____

_____

_____

_____

_____

_____

_____

_____

_____

_____

_____

_____

_____

Self-Check

How Do You Feel Right Now?
Write About It.

_____

_____

_____

_____

_____

_____

_____

_____

_____

_____

_____

_____

_____

_____

_____

_____

_____

_____

Say and Do Things That Enhance Those You're Engaging With. You Always Bring the Highest Peak Possible to the Forefront of Your Interactions. Always Leave People Better Than You Found Them.

~Yvette Malveaux

Day Twenty-Three

I Won't be Held Down

What is it you do that makes YOU bounce back to YOURSELF?

_____

_____

_____

_____

_____

_____

_____

_____

_____

_____

_____

_____

_____

_____

_____

_____

_____

_____

Self-Check

How Do You Feel Right Now?
Write About It.

_____

_____

_____

_____

_____

_____

_____

_____

_____

_____

_____

_____

_____

_____

_____

_____

_____

Do Your Best to Recognize Your Moments of Opportunity to Lead.

Fill Them with Quality Conversations and Actions.

~Yvette Malveaux

Day Twenty-Four

Modifying my Future

What change would YOU make to YOUR life today?

_____

_____

_____

_____

_____

_____

_____

_____

_____

_____

_____

_____

_____

_____

_____

_____

_____

_____

Self-Check

How Do You Feel Right Now? Write About It.

_____

_____

_____

_____

_____

_____

_____

_____

_____

_____

_____

_____

_____

_____

_____

Plan to Keep Moving and Doing Great Things in Your Life.

Always Choose What You Are Going to Do Next...

There's So Much You Can Actually Do, You Only Need to Choose What You're Going to Do.

~Yvette Malveaux

Day Twenty-Five

How I See Myself

How do YOU see Yourself? Describe YOURSELF in YOUR own words.

_____

_____

_____

_____

_____

_____

_____

_____

_____

_____

_____

_____

_____

_____

_____

_____

_____

_____

Self-Check

How Do You Feel Right Now?
Write About It.

_____

_____

_____

_____

_____

_____

_____

_____

_____

_____

_____

_____

_____

_____

_____

I See You, and You Are

* Beautiful *

~Yvette Malveaux

Day Twenty-Six

Making a Plan

What Is it that YOU know YOU should be doing?

_____

_____

_____

_____

_____

_____

_____

_____

_____

_____

_____

_____

_____

_____

_____

_____

_____

Self-Check

How Do You Feel Right Now? Write About It.

_____

_____

_____

_____

_____

_____

_____

_____

_____

_____

_____

_____

_____

_____

_____

_____

You Learn

You Grow

You Change

DON'T YOU DARE
REMAIN THE SAME!

~Yvette Malveaux

Day Twenty-Seven

Facing my Fears

What Are YOU Scared of? Is it people, places, or things? Or are YOU scared of YOURSELF?

_____

_____

_____

_____

_____

_____

_____

_____

_____

_____

_____

_____

_____

_____

_____

_____

_____

Self-Check

How Do You Feel Right Now?
Write About It.

_____

_____

_____

_____

_____

_____

_____

_____

_____

_____

_____

_____

_____

_____

*Never Stop Feeling Good
About Yourself. Become the very
point of contact that you needed
In Your Own Life.*

~Yvette Malveaux

Day Twenty-Eight

Loving My Younger Self

What would YOU say to YOUR younger self?

_____

_____

_____

_____

_____

_____

_____

_____

_____

_____

_____

_____

_____

_____

_____

_____

_____

_____

Self-Check

How Do You Feel Right Now?
Write About It.

_____

_____

_____

_____

_____

_____

_____

_____

_____

_____

_____

_____

_____

_____

_____

Wherever You Are, Use Your Time, Energy, and Talents to Do the Best You Can Right Now.

~Yvette Malveaux

Day Twenty- Nine

I Enjoy my Life

What are the little things in YOUR Life that YOU enjoy?

_____

_____

_____

_____

_____

_____

_____

_____

_____

_____

_____

_____

_____

_____

_____

_____

_____

Self-Check

How Do You Feel Right Now?
Write About It.

_____

_____

_____

_____

_____

_____

_____

_____

_____

_____

_____

_____

_____

_____

_____

_____

_____

Nobody Has Everything,
But Everybody Has Something.
Use What You Have Right Now.
Use It Wisely, Use It Freely and Use
It with Love.

~Yvette Malveaux

Day Thirty

I am Living in my Now

When is the last time YOU were truly present in YOUR own life?

_____

_____

_____

_____

_____

_____

_____

_____

_____

_____

_____

_____

_____

_____

_____

_____

_____

Self-Check

How Do You Feel Right Now? Write About It.

_____

_____

_____

_____

_____

_____

_____

_____

_____

_____

_____

_____

_____

_____

_____

_____

_____

_____

_____

The Essence of Knowledge is Using it to Do Great Things.

~Yvette Malveaux

Day Thirty-One

I am Successful

What is something YOU truly want to be known for?

_____

_____

_____

_____

_____

_____

_____

_____

_____

_____

_____

_____

_____

_____

_____

_____

_____

Self-Check

How Do You Feel Right Now?
Write About It.

_____

_____

_____

_____

_____

_____

_____

_____

_____

_____

_____

_____

_____

_____

_____

_____

_____

_____

*Find Your Zone and Unpack
All You've Got!*

~Yvette Malveaux

The Unload Zone

This is where YOU get the trash, clutter, and nonsense from the inside of YOU, to the outside. Then YOU can sort through YOUR inner conversations and beliefs and throw the things away that need to be thrown out. See and hear for YOURSELF the things YOU have missed or overlooked.

In this zone, YOU will be able to see things clearer and be able to change what needs to be changed, upgraded, or dusted off. YOU will see what needs to be kept as well. This is a type of spring cleaning for YOUR soul and wellbeing.

These next pages will be for SELF venting, to rid YOURSELF of the things YOU have been stuffing within. Like YOUR feelings and thoughts, so YOU can get clarity and perspective on YOURSELF.

This writing assignment is all about YOU. It has nothing to do with pointing YOUR finger towards anything except what YOU can do to get YOU better. How YOU can change the trajectory of YOUR life and circumstances?

It's accountability, ownership, and responsibility of SELF for the purpose and intent of living YOUR life totally aware of who YOU are and being fully aware of how things are affecting YOU, and how YOU are feeling. What are YOU going to do about what's going on within and around YOU?

Be sure to not only vent but come up with solutions to the situations YOU have discovered. You have had YOUR answers all along. They were only shrouded by the buildup; that is what is so great about taking the time to do this writing assignment.

ZONE TIP... Don't Lie to Yourself. You are YOUR most important ally.

Be bold, Be daring, Be true to YOURSELF.

DATE_____

VENT SESSIONS IN THE UNLOAD ZONE
FIRE AWAY...

_____

_____

_____

_____

_____

_____

_____

_____

_____

_____

_____

_____

_____

_____

_____

_____

_____

_____

SOLUTIONS AND ANSWERS TO YOUR SELF RANT
What are YOU going to do about it?

_____

_____

_____

_____

_____

_____

_____

_____

_____

_____

_____

_____

_____

_____

_____

_____

_____

_____

_____

_____

DATE_____

VENT SESSIONS IN THE UNLOAD ZONE
FIRE AWAY...

_____

_____

_____

_____

_____

_____

_____

_____

_____

_____

_____

_____

_____

_____

_____

_____

_____

SOLUTIONS AND ANSWERS TO YOUR SELF RANT
What are YOU going to do about it?

_____

_____

_____

_____

_____

_____

_____

_____

_____

_____

_____

_____

_____

_____

_____

_____

_____

_____

_____

DATE_____

VENT SESSIONS IN THE UNLOAD ZONE
FIRE AWAY...

_____

_____

_____

_____

_____

_____

_____

_____

_____

_____

_____

_____

_____

_____

_____

_____

_____

_____

_____

SOLUTIONS AND ANSWERS TO YOUR SELF RANT
What are YOU going to do about it?

_____

_____

_____

_____

_____

_____

_____

_____

_____

_____

_____

_____

_____

_____

_____

_____

_____

_____

_____

VENT SESSIONS IN THE UNLOAD ZONE
FIRE AWAY...

_____

_____

_____

_____

_____

_____

_____

_____

_____

_____

_____

_____

_____

_____

_____

_____

SOLUTIONS AND ANSWERS TO YOUR SELF RANT
What are YOU going to do about it?

_____

_____

_____

_____

_____

_____

_____

_____

_____

_____

_____

_____

_____

_____

_____

_____

_____

_____

_____

VENT SESSIONS IN THE UNLOAD ZONE
FIRE AWAY...

_____

_____

_____

_____

_____

_____

_____

_____

_____

_____

_____

_____

_____

_____

_____

_____

_____

_____

SOLUTIONS AND ANSWERS TO YOUR SELF RANT
What are YOU going to do about it?

_____

_____

_____

_____

_____

_____

_____

_____

_____

_____

_____

_____

_____

_____

_____

_____

_____

_____

_____

_____

_____

DATE_____

VENT SESSIONS IN THE UNLOAD ZONE
FIRE AWAY...

_____

_____

_____

_____

_____

_____

_____

_____

_____

_____

_____

_____

_____

_____

_____

_____

_____

_____

SOLUTIONS AND ANSWERS TO YOUR SELF RANT
What are YOU going to do about it?

_____

_____

_____

_____

_____

_____

_____

_____

_____

_____

_____

_____

_____

_____

_____

_____

_____

_____

_____

_____

DATE_____

VENT SESSIONS IN THE UNLOAD ZONE
FIRE AWAY...

_____

_____

_____

_____

_____

_____

_____

_____

_____

_____

_____

_____

_____

_____

_____

_____

_____

_____

SOLUTIONS AND ANSWERS TO YOUR SELF RANT
What are YOU going to do about it?

_____

_____

_____

_____

_____

_____

_____

_____

_____

_____

_____

_____

_____

_____

_____

_____

_____

_____

_____

_____

DATE_____

VENT SESSIONS IN THE UNLOAD ZONE
FIRE AWAY...

_____

_____

_____

_____

_____

_____

_____

_____

_____

_____

_____

_____

_____

_____

_____

_____

_____

_____

SOLUTIONS AND ANSWERS TO YOUR SELF RANT
What are YOU going to do about it?

_____

_____

_____

_____

_____

_____

_____

_____

_____

_____

_____

_____

_____

_____

_____

_____

_____

_____

_____

_____

DATE_____

VENT SESSIONS IN THE UNLOAD ZONE
FIRE AWAY...

_____

_____

_____

_____

_____

_____

_____

_____

_____

_____

_____

_____

_____

_____

_____

_____

SOLUTIONS AND ANSWERS TO YOUR SELF RANT
What are YOU going to do about it?

_____

_____

_____

_____

_____

_____

_____

_____

_____

_____

_____

_____

_____

_____

_____

_____

_____

_____

_____

_____

_____

DATE_____

VENT SESSIONS IN THE UNLOAD ZONE
FIRE AWAY...

_____
_____
_____
_____
_____
_____
_____
_____
_____
_____
_____
_____
_____
_____
_____
_____
_____
_____
_____

SOLUTIONS AND ANSWERS TO YOUR SELF RANT
What are YOU going to do about it?

_____

_____

_____

_____

_____

_____

_____

_____

_____

_____

_____

_____

_____

_____

_____

_____

_____

_____

_____

*Let My Words Be More
Than Motivation,
Let Them Carry Life!*

~Yvette Malveaux

There is really no limitation on who you are. The only limitation is what people choose to focus on. Your greatness isn't intimidating when you show it. It just causes others to realize they haven't tapped into their own and that's the part that intimidates. They haven't put the work in. You paid a price for what you know and who you are. You didn't give up or cut corners, and apparently you didn't run from it and hide. You stood.

Whether you had the answers at those times or not, you showed up and were very visible. That counts. Even today, when there's still things to do, problems to solve, and commitments to keep, you still show up and come through.

If someone labels you anything other than who you are and what you have displayed, they are not really seeing you through the right lens. What they see is their limitations, because they couldn't reciprocate the same dedication to commit to follow through and to know that they too should at least put forth an effort to show up and bring some viable actions, conversations, and deeds to the forefront as well.

~*Yvette Malveaux*

Made in the USA
Middletown, DE
17 September 2020

19257908R00179